EAT LIKE THIS.

SIMPLIFYING HEALTHY MEAL PREP
FOR EVERY DIET IN YOUR HOUSEHOLD

Gluten-free, dairy-free, soy-free, and corn-free recipes to nurture your gut and open your mind.
Flexible recipes to accommodate the various dietary needs of everyone in your household.

Written by Rebekah G. Eisner
Certified Empowerment Coach
www.rgec.life

Photography & Design by Anthony Giacomino
Illustrated by Abigail Eisner
Layout & Assembly by Tikva Lightner
Edited by Carrie Wiss & Linda Kelley

To those who believe in me: my devoted husband Ben and my supportive daughters Elizabeth, Abigail, and Emma. Also to the clients—present and future—who entrust me to be a part of their healing journey. **This book is for you!**

GOOD FOOD | HEALTHY LIFE

I grew up around considerably healthy food. We were poor, so my mom had a huge garden, and we raised goats for milk. Everything was made from scratch. Whether we were making bread, fermenting yogurt, cooking up a batch of applesauce, or canning vegetables, there was always some production happening in our kitchen, and the smells were delicious!.

By the time I was a teenager, we had more money, and it was a luxury to be able to buy processed foods. It was empowering for me to get to eat what my social contemporaries ate, so I joined in on the Standard American Diet (SAD). Poor digestion became a part of my life, and I didn't realize how unhealthy my gut really was.

story.

At age 19, I met my soulmate, Ben. We married and started a family right away. Having three daughters in a row was not good for me emotionally or hormonally. What's more, since I was raised in a large family and had a sibling with cerebral palsy who required a lot of additional care, I stuffed my emotions and just "pushed through" life so I wouldn't be a bother. Overdoing it was all I knew, and saying "no" was not part of my vocabulary. I was chronically fatigued, but still "pushing through." Four-hour-long naps were not uncommon for me once all three girls were in school.

FUNCTIONAL MEDICINE

During this time, one of my friends whose symptoms of chronic fatigue sounded similar to mine told me about her functional medicine doctor, Dr. Meress, so I went to see him. After a battery of tests, he discovered that I had a hormonal imbalance. He used hormone therapy along with supplementation to balance me out. He also told me that I was "FOS" (full of shit). What he meant by that was even though I was a skinny girl, my colon was not eliminating properly, and that was toxic to my body.

In the meantime, Ben had been ignoring some serious health issues for several years. He had experienced fainting spells and paralysis on one side of his face. Some of his doctors suspected that he had multiple sclerosis. The idea of being diagnosed with MS terrified him, so he buried his head and silently hoped his symptoms would just go away.

Even though he was depressed and suffered daily fatigue, Ben wouldn't go to a doctor. Finally, after ignoring symptoms for too long, he started losing color saturation in his vision. It hurt his eyes to move them from side to side. An opthamologist found that he had an inflamed optic nerve and sent him to a neurologist. Through an MRI, the neurologist discovered that Ben had lesions on his brain. Ben decided he wasn't convinced he had MS, the diagnosis this seemed to be leading to. He wanted

a second opinion and decided to see my functional doctor. Through tons of testing and blood work, we found out that Ben had Lyme disease.

As Ben went through a three-year treatment plan, his symptoms, including the lesions on his brain, went away. We were elated that Ben's illness had been identified and treated, but we found our chaotic lifestyle was still having an impact on his health. Stress would trigger the Lyme to flare up every couple of years, and Ben would experience another bout of being bound to the couch with debilitating symptoms and threat of losing his vision.

IT WAS TIME TO MAKE A CHANGE

Fear for Ben's life led me to ask our doctor if there was anything we could do in the way of diet to combat his Lyme disease from another angle. He introduced us to Dr. Abfall, the naturopathic doctor who worked in his clinic. Dr. Abfall used electro-dermal screening to pinpoint foods that were stressors to Ben's body and could add to the inflammation that was keeping his immune system from functioning at maximum levels. Based on her recommendations, we cut out gluten, dairy, corn, and soy, along with other foods that showed up in her analysis. This was not an easy process. Cooking was a major part of my life already, and I thought we were healthy. Ben resented the fact that he had to cut foods he loved out of his diet, and he would be annoyed after we left the appointments with Dr. Abfall. In spite of this, he was resolved to kick the Lyme disease, so he stuck with these lifestyle changes like a champ.

At this point, our girls were in the pre-teen phase of life. They were upset about the changes I made in the kitchen. The food tasted weird to them, but I wasn't able to cook multiple meals. Cooking in a new way was stressful enough, so whatever I made was what the whole family would have to eat. When friends came over, our girls were embarrassed by the way we ate. But after several months, I learned new recipes that satisfied our whole family, and we started to enjoy the new way of eating. It has been a long process, but now we prefer this style of eating and enjoy food much more than we used to.

HAPPY AND HEALTHY

To this day, everyone in our family feels better than ever. My digestion has completely normalized. During this process, I worked to take control of our health and learned things about myself that I would never have discovered had I not gone through this frightening experience. In changing the trajectory of my own life and that of my family's, I discovered a passion to empower others to take control of their lives and discover what makes them thrive. As I write this book, our girls are all in college, and they love to cook for themselves. They have also learned to use their voices and advocate for getting their needs met so they can make the food that helps them feel their best while living on college campuses that don't cater to the eating habits they've chosen to adopt.

Ben has been symptom-free for seven years, and we attribute this largely to the health of his gut in addition to the medical care he received. Throughout this process, we all have learned to better listen to our guts. Eating foods that contribute to our gut health has led us to trust our mind/gut connection and be more in tune with our intuition. This has enabled us to slow down and not live in constant chaos. While learning to be intuitive to foods that make our bodies feel their best, we have found that we have chosen to eat different diets, even though we may be living under the same roof.

THIS COOKBOOK

This cookbook is a collection of recipes that have become our go-to's in our household. My hope is that our journey, and the years of practice I put into learning to cook in a practical, healthy way, will benefit you as you embark on a journey of your own. Throughout this book, I will use these symbols to let you know when a recipe is already dairy free, vegan, vegetarian, paleo, or uses a slow cooker. The symbols are also used when there is an option to make it dairy free, vegan, vegetarian, or paleo if it isn't already.

DAIRY FREE   VEGAN   VEGETARIAN   PALEO   SLOW COOKER

THE "EAT LIKE THIS" DIET

There are so many diet trends today that can help people with autoimmune and other diseases and food sensitivities live better lives. For a while, my family and I stuck with a Paleo diet. Now that we have a couple of family members who follow a vegan diet, I've had to adapt to a mix of diets. In doing so, I've gathered a collection of healthy, delicious, and practical recipes that can be adapted for the spectrum of meat and non-meat eaters, and everything in between.

This book is a curation of recipes and ideas for making food preparation more enjoyable and to support my followers of the "Eat Like This" diet who are trying to eliminate the major inflammatory foods while catering to different eating styles under one roof.

The first goal of eating like this, is to learn how to break the rules around "dieting," and to allow others to do the same. There are so many fad diets out there that create confusion, shame, and failure. Becoming in tune with yourself is meant to bring freedom in the area of food, while also creating a healthy, balanced, and more fulfilling lifestyle. My desire for you is that you will learn to eat real, whole foods that make you feel your best, rather than feeling guilt over not adhering to what someone tells you is the "right" way to eat. This will be assessed through self-reflective journaling and guidelines for restructuring your pantry. It's my hope that you'll literally watch your life change before your eyes!

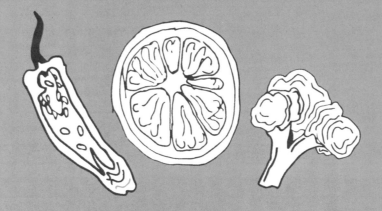

TABLE OF CONTENTS

DINNER RECIPES

POTATO & PROTEIN BOWLS

DESSERTS

SNACKS & APPETIZERS

VI. NOTES

Get ready

SELF-REFLECTION

The following exercise is meant to help you think about where you are now and envision where you want to be as you pursue the "Eat Like This" lifestyle. Being able to visualize and document what that lifestyle might feel like can spur on the motivation to begin making changes you desire to make.

JOURNAL EXERCISE | ENVISION YOUR LIFE

Take a few minutes to envision your life 1 month from now. What do you want to change, and how will you go about making those changes? How do you want to feel after you've made them? Write all these things down in a journal.

Next, look 6 months into the future. How would you like to feel in your body? What might your body look like? Would feeling better internally affect other areas of your life? Journal about these things as well.

Purging phase

CLEANING OUT YOUR PANTRY

Now it's time to clean out your pantry. If you start feeling overwhelmed, remember the way you want to feel and go back to that. This will give you motivation and a vision for why you are making these changes for yourself.

Pull out all of your food and start reading labels. If you don't feel comfortable throwing food away, donate food to a charity, compost it, or give it to a neighbor.

First, look for cane sugar in the ingredients. Four grams of sugar is equal to 1 teaspoon of sugar. (That's equivalent to eating 1 whole sugar cube.) Next, look for wheat, corn*, soy, and dairy. These are the biggest problem foods that lead to internal inflammation and chronic disease[†]. Get rid of any foods in your pantry with these ingredients.

Now, put everything back that does not have the ingredients named above, and give yourself a pat on the back. You're on the way to a healthier and more wholesome you!

CLEANING OUT YOUR FRIDGE

After you've finished with the pantry, it's time to move on to the fridge following the same guidelines.

JOURNAL EXERCISE | PURGING

How did it feel to do this exercise? Did you experience any emotions? Take a minute and journal about your experience of throwing out (or giving away) the food you got rid of. How was it for you?

_____

_____

_____

_____

_____

_____

_____

_____

_____

_____

_____

_____

_____

_____

_____

_____

_____

_____

_____

_____

_____

_____

_____

_____

_____

_____

_____

_____

_____

_____

_____

_____

_____

*Eating sprouted corn once in awhile could be an option—the brand Food for Life® has sprouted corn tortillas.

†Blum, Susan. *The Immune System Recovery Plan: A Doctor's 4-Step Program to Treat Autoimmune Disease.* New York, NY: Scribner, 2013.

Get Set

Now it's time to get stocked up on the right supplies so you'll be ready to get going in the kitchen.

ESSENTIAL TOOLS

A few good quality knives (chopping/pairing)

Cutting board

Baking sheet

Muffin tin

Good quality blender

Food processor

Measuring cups

Measuring spoons

Mixing bowls

Parchment paper

Lemon press

Serving bowls & plates

Serving spoons

Spatulas

Whisk

Pots and pans

Slow Cooker

Roasting pan

Mason jars (about 1 dozen)

BASIC SPICES

Sea salt

Black pepper

Cayenne

Cumin

Paprika

Oregano

Chili powder

Vanilla powder

Cinnamon

Coriander

Cardamom

Fennel seeds

Bay leaves

Onion powder

Garlic powder

Turmeric

Baking soda

Baking powder

BASIC VEGETABLES
(best to buy organic if possible)

Lettuce

Kale

Zucchini

Carrots

Onions

Garlic

Celery

Broccoli

Butternut squash

Mini peppers

Brussels sprouts

Cauliflower

BASIC FRUITS
(best to buy organic if possible)

Green apples	Frozen blueberries	Cucumber
Bananas	Avocado	

BASIC PANTRY FOODS

Cashew butter	Cashews	Wild rice
Almond butter	Almonds	Quinoa
Sunflower seed butter	Other nuts	Kombu (an edible kelp)
Tahini	Sunflower seeds	Canned coconut milk
Ghee	Hemp seeds	Olive oil
Almond flour	Chia seeds	Coconut oil
Coconut flour	Pumpkin seeds	Sriracha hot chili sauce
Enjoy Life® mini chocolate chips	Tomato puree	Tabasco Sauce®
Stevia	Dried black beans	Nutritional yeast
Arrowroot powder	Dried garbanzo beans (chickpeas)	Ume plum vinegar
Monk fruit sweetener	Sprouted brown rice	Lentils

BASIC REFRIGERATOR FOODS

Unsweetened nut beverage (coconut, almond, or cashew)	Fermented pickles (Bubbies® is my favorite brand)	Apple cider vinegar
Lemons	Cauliflower rice	Dijon mustard
Limes	Tamari sauce (gluten-free soy sauce)	Vegenaise® (egg-free, gluten-free mayonnaise)
Sauerkraut	Gluten-free, soy-free miso	Olives

JOURNAL EXERCISE | ACTION STEPS

What holds you back from planning meals and making a grocery list ahead of time? What would help you take an action step to make time for this? What day of the week is best for you to plan your meals? What day is best for shopping? What are your favorite stores for food shopping? Do you need to make more than one list; one for each store? Take a few minutes to think about these questions and journal your thoughts and feelings.

_____

_____

_____

_____

_____

_____

_____

_____

_____

_____

_____

_____

_____

_____

_____

_____

_____

_____

_____

_____

DIRTY DOZEN

(Taken from Environmental Working Group, www.foodnews.org)

The 12 most contaminated/genetically modified fruits and veggies, when not organic:

Peach	Strawberry	Carrot
Apple	Cherry	Pear
Bell pepper	Kale	Buy organic!
Celery	Lettuce	
Nectarine	Grapes (imported)	

CLEAN 15

The 15 least contaminated fruits and veggies:

Onion	Asparagus	Papaya
Avocado	Sweet peas	Watermelon
Sweet corn	Kiwi	Broccoli
Pineapple	Cabbage	Tomato
Mango	Eggplant	Sweet potato

Time to organize

PLANNING MEALS AND FOOD PREP

The beginning of the week is the best time to plan out what you want to eat for the week (I like to do this on Sundays). Not only does a weekly meal plan make your week easier, it also helps you stick to your commitment to yourself and your health. If you are only cooking for one or two people, you may only want to cook 3 times during the week and eat leftovers on the other evenings. Let's get going!

Take a moment and get your calendar out. Mark a time and day of the week where you can sit down and plan your menus and grocery list. Having it on the calendar holds you to it.

Look through each recipe category—breakfast, lunch, and dinner—and see what inspires you.

Mark the pages that stand out to you. Then write down what you want to eat each morning, afternoon, and evening. Write down the page number for each recipe and start making your shopping list for the week. When you've finished planning your meals and creating your grocery list, take a few minutes and journal about how it felt to do it. Then head out to the grocery store (or mark the time slot in your calendar when you are planning on going).

SAMPLE WEEKLY MENU

MONDAY

Breakfast: Hearty Seed Bread with Fruity Nut Spread

Lunch: Mason Jar Salad

Dinner: Buddha Bowl with Tahini Dressing

TUESDAY

Breakfast: Bacon & Egg "Cupcakes"

Lunch: Salmon Salad on Hearty Seed Bread

Dinner: Chicken Soup (reserve 1 cup broth for Slow Cooker Pork Shoulder)

WEDNESDAY

Breakfast: Slow Cooker Oatmeal

Lunch: Mason Jar Salad with leftover Salmon Salad

Dinner: Slow Cooker Pork Shoulder

THURSDAY

Breakfast: Leftover Slow Cooker Oatmeal

Lunch: Pulled Pork Wrap (using leftover Pork Shoulder)

Dinner: Build-Your-Own Pizza

FRIDAY

Breakfast: Kale Smoothie

Lunch: Build-Your-Own Mashed Sweet Potato

Dinner: Out with friends

SATURDAY

Breakfast: Avocado Toast with Hearty Seed Bread

Lunch: Paleo "Tortilla" Wrap with turkey, lettuce & avocado

Dinner: Slow Cooker Tomatillo Chicken with rice, beans, and guacamole

Dessert: Macadamia Chocolate Chip Cookies

SUNDAY

Breakfast: Veggie Hash with Eggs

Lunch: Leftovers

Dinner: Veggie Stir-Fry with Cauliflower Rice

SAMPLE GROCERY LIST

(Create this by looking over your menus and taking inventory of what you have on hand and what you will need for your meals. This list assumes you have some of the ingredients on hand.)

Coconut yogurt	Carrots	Bacon
Canned wild salmon	Onion	Eggs
Gluten-free wraps (or ingredients to make your own)	Butternut squash	Sunflower seeds
Almond beverage	Broccoli	Almonds
Cauliflower rice	Chocolate chips	Psyllium husk powder
Lettuce	Chicken thighs (bone-in)	Gluten free oats
Kale	Whole chicken	Bay leaves
Broccoli	Pancetta	Frozen blueberries

WEEKLY CHOPPING AND FOOD PREP

After your meals are planned and you have all of your ingredients, take an extra 30 minutes at the beginning of the week to chop your veggies*. This will save you LOADS of time, while making mealtime much easier and stress free.

Instead of being a chore, cooking should be a time for fun, self-expression, and quality time with your partner or other family members. Turn on some music. Break out some dance moves, even! Get out your cutting board, knife, vegetables, and Mason jars. Start with one veggie at a time, give each one its own jar, and then place the jars in the refrigerator. It's lovely to see an organized variety of fresh veggies when you open the fridge.

You can store your grains and flours the same way. Label them in Mason jars before storing them in your pantry.

To save time during the week, you can make a batch of Hearty Seed Bread (page 37) and Paleo Tortilla Wraps (page 35) to keep in the freezer. Coconut Yogurt (page 32) and Big Batch Beans (page 48) are other things you could make at this time. Look ahead to see what prep will help you the most with the recipes you're making during the upcoming week.

*Save scraps from your vegetables as you chop. These can be used in Veggie Broth (page 46).

JOURNAL EXERCISE | PREPARING

You're getting so close! Now, take a moment and journal your thoughts and feelings about your experience with preparing your food for the week.

Star's Lemonade

This elixir has many health benefits. It is immune-boosting, liver cleansing, alkalizing and slimming.*

WELLNESS ELIXIR | **5 MIN**

 EASY | SERVES 1

Ingredients

1 lemon

10 ounces warm or room temperature water

Nickel size slice of ginger root, peeled

½ teaspoon honey

Small pinch cayenne pepper

Directions:
Combine all ingredients and stir well.
Remove the ginger after 5 minutes.

*www.drmanand.com

Virus Vigilante

When you feel like you are coming down with a bug, take this elixir to boost your immune system.*

WELLNESS ELIXIR

 5 MIN

EASY

SERVES 4

Ingredients

1 organic green apple

Juice of 1 lemon

1 inch piece of ginger, peeled

1 clove garlic

1 teaspoon vitamin C powder or camu powder

8 ounces water

Directions:
Combine all ingredients in a blender and blend until well incorporated.

  *www.healthline.com/nutrition/camu-camu#2-contains-powerful-antioxiidants www.webmd.com/food-recipes/benefits-apples#1

Building Block Basics

Dairy-Free Coconut Yogurt

BUILDING BLOCK BASIC **30 HRS**
largely unattended

EASY | YIELDS 1 QUART

Ingredients

2 (14-ounce) cans coconut milk

2 teaspoons agar agar flakes,
or 2 tablespoons tapioca starch
(see recipe notes)

4 probiotic capsules or 4 tablespoons store-bought coconut yogurt

Directions:

Warm the oven for about 5 minutes, until it reaches about 100°F, then turn the oven off, but leave the oven light on.

Make sure the jars you are using have been sterilized.

Shake the can of coconut milk before opening, then pour it into a medium-sized saucepan. Whisk until the milk is smooth. Sprinkle 1 teaspoon of agar agar flakes over the coconut milk, and let it sit without stirring.

If you prefer to use tapioca starch, transfer 1/3 cup coconut milk to a bowl and add the starch. Whisk this together until the starch is dissolved, then pour back into the saucepan.

Place saucepan on the stove over medium heat, and warm until the mixture starts to simmer (the agar agar will start to melt into the coconut milk). Whisk, then turn the heat to low.

Continue cooking on low, whisking occasionally for 5 to 10 minutes, until the agar agar flakes are dissolved or the tapioca starch mixture has thickened. Cool until the milk is lukewarm, about 100°F.

Open the probiotic capsule and pour the contents into the milk. Whisk to combine. *Another option is to whisk in 4 tablespoons of store-bought coconut yogurt.*

Pour the mixture into sterilized jars, and then fasten lids on the jars. Place in the oven with the oven light on. This creates the perfect temperature for fermentation. *You can use a yogurt maker or place into a dehydrator at 110°F.* Leave jars in oven for 12 to 24 hours to allow fermentation to take place. Once the yogurt has set, put the jars in the fridge and chill for at least 6 hours. The yogurt will become thicker as it chills. If the mixture separates, stir. Store in the fridge for up to 2 weeks.

If the yogurt develops a pink or grey discoloration on its surface, that means it has been contaminated with bad bacteria and should be discarded.

Paleo "Tortillia Wraps"

BUILDING BLOCK BASIC | 15 MIN

EASY | 12 WRAPS

Ingredients

6 large eggs, beaten

1 cup almond milk

6 tablespoons coconut flour, sifted

½ cup arrowroot powder

2 tablespoons melted ghee

½ teaspoon sea salt

Ghee or palm shortening for the pan

Directions:

Heat an 8-inch crepe pan or griddle to medium-high heat.

Combine the eggs, almond milk, coconut flour, arrowroot powder, ghee, and salt together, then whisk. Allow the batter to rest for 10 minutes, then whisk again. Melt a little ghee in the pan and spread evenly. Ladle 1/4 cup batter onto the hot pan. Tip slightly and turn the pan quickly, letting the batter spread evenly. Fill in any holes with a smidge of batter. Cook until the edges of the tortilla start to lift, about 45 seconds, then gently flip the wrap. Cook for approximately 30 seconds on the other side. Place on a plate to cool. Repeat the steps until all of the batter is used, adding more ghee to the pan between wraps when needed.

The wraps will keep in the refrigerator for 5 days or the freezer for 6 months. Place a piece of parchment paper between the wraps and seal in a resealable bag. Thaw in the refrigerator for 2 hours before using.

   *Dairy-free option: use palm shortening instead of butter

Hearty Seed Bread

This recipe is from my dear friend Vivienne, who lives in New Zealand. She has always inspired me with her ability to create tasty meals out of simple ingredients.

BUILDING BLOCK BASIC	**3 HRS** largely unattended
EASY	12 SLICES

Ingredients

1 cup sunflower seeds

½ cup hemp seeds

½ cup almonds, chopped

1 ½ cups gluten-free rolled oats

2 tablespoons sesame seeds

3 tablespoons psyllium husk powder

1 teaspoon fine-grain sea salt

1 tablespoon honey or molasses

3 tablespoons melted coconut oil

1 ½ cups water

Directions:

Line a loaf pan with parchment paper. In a medium mixing bowl, combine all of the dry ingredients and stir well. In a small mixing bowl, combine honey, coconut oil, and water and whisk. Stir wet ingredients into dry ingredients and mix well. Place the dough in the prepared loaf pan and press down until evenly distributed.

Allow the dough to sit on the counter for 2 to 12 hours. When ready, the dough should retain its shape when you lift the parchment paper.

Preheat oven to 350 degrees. Place the loaf pan on the middle rack of the oven. Bake for 20 minutes. Remove the bread from the pan and place upside-down, directly on the oven rack. Bake for another 30 - 40 minutes. When done, the bread will sound hollow when tapped. Allow the bread to cool completely before slicing.

Slice the loaf, then freeze. Use as needed throughout the week.

  *Vegan option, use molasses instead of honey

Tomato Pizza Sauce

Ingredients:

½ yellow onion, pureéd

2 medium-sized garlic cloves, minced

28 ounce can crushed tomatoes

2 teaspoon salt

½ teaspoon pepper

1 teaspoon crushed peppers

1 tablespoon dried oregano

Directions:

Heat oil over medium heat in a saucepan. Add onions and garlic and sauté until transparent, about 3 minutes. Add the tomatoes, salt, pepper, crushed red peppers, and oregano. Reduce heat to low and simmer for 15 minutes.

Flatbread Pizza Crust

BUILDING BLOCK BASIC 25 MIN

EASY | SERVES 2-3

Ingredients

1 cup arrowroot starch or tapioca flour

⅓ cup coconut flour

¼ teaspoon salt

½ cup canned coconut milk

¼ cup olive oil

⅛ cup olive oil

3 small cloves garlic, pressed or minced

1 egg

(※ ½ cup olive oil)
total

Directions:

Preheat oven to 500 degrees.

Combine arrowroot starch, coconut flour, and ¼ teaspoon salt in a medium mixing bowl and whisk. Heat the coconut milk, olive oil, and garlic in a small saucepan over medium heat. Remove from heat when it just comes to a simmer.

Add liquid ingredients to dry ingredients and stir to combine.

In a separate bowl, whisk the egg. Add the whisked egg to the dough and mix thoroughly. Let the dough rest for 5 minutes. Spread the dough in a thin layer on a baking sheet that is lined with parchment paper. (Another option is to divide the dough into 2 - 3 smaller individual pizzas).

Bake for 10 minutes. Remove and add your toppings of choice (See Build-Your-Own-Pizza, page 110. Bake for an additional 10 - 15 minutes, until crust is golden.

   *Dairy-free option: use palm shortening instead of butter

Macadamia Nut Butter

BUILDING BLOCK BASIC 5 MIN

🥄 EASY | YIELDS 2 CUPS

Ingredients

2 cups raw macadamia nuts

Directions:

Puree the macadamia nuts in a food processor or high-speed blender until smooth. This can be stored in an airtight container in the refrigerator for up to 1 week.

Almond Paste

BUILDING BLOCK BASIC 5 MIN

🥄 EASY | YIELDS 1 CUP

Ingredients

1 ½ cup blanched almonds

1 cup monk fruit sweetener

1 large egg white (lightly beaten)

1 teaspoon almond extract

Directions:

Place the almonds and ½ cup sugar in a food processor with steel blade attachment. Process until finely ground. Scrape the sides of the food processor as needed. Add the rest of the sugar, and pulse a few times to incorporate all of the sugar. Add the egg white and almond extract, and process until a paste is formed. Wrap in plastic wrap and store in fridge for up to a week or in freezer for up to 6 months.

Basil Pesto

BUILDING BLOCK BASIC | 5 MIN

EASY | 1/2 CUP

Ingredients

4 small cloves garlic

approximately 2 cups basil leaves,
rinsed and dried

⅓ cup extra virgin olive oil

½ teaspoon salt

½ teaspoon freshly ground black pepper

Directions:

Chop the garlic cloves by dropping them through the feeding tube of a food processor while the motor is running. Turn the food processor off, remove the lid, and add the basil to the bowl. Process again and, with the motor running, slowly drizzle the oil through the feeding tube and process until the basil is pureed. Transfer the pesto to a bowl, and stir in the salt and pepper. Cover and refrigerate until ready to use (can be stored in the refrigerator for 2 to 3 days).

"Queso" Cashew Sauce

BUILDING BLOCK BASIC	5 MIN
EASY	YIELDS 2 CUPS

Ingredients

1 ½ cups raw cashew pieces

1 jalapeño, seeded (optional)

¼ cup nutritional yeast

¾ tsp salt

¼ teaspoon garlic powder

¾ cup water

3 tablespoons lemon juice

Directions:

Chop the jalapeno by dropping it through the feeding tube of a food processor while the motor is running. Add the cashews and pulse to a fine powder. Add in the remaining ingredients and process until smooth.

* I leave the seeds in my jalapeño for extra spice

Black Bean Pesto

These beans can be used as a spread or dip. They can also be used in the wraps, on Tostadas (page 104), or in or in Mucho Bowls (page 99). When heated through, use as a side. Garnish with cilantro.

BUILDING BLOCK BASIC	5 MIN
EASY	YIELDS 2 CUPS

Ingredients

3 cups cooked black beans from Big-Batch Beans, with ½ to 1 cup cooking liquid (page 48)

1 jalapeno pepper, seeded

1 clove garlic

Stems from one bunch cilantro

Sea salt and ground pepper

Directions:

Chop the garlic clove and jalapeno by dropping them through the feeding tube of a food processor while the motor is running. Add the beans and cilantro stems. Puree, adding bean liquid slowly, until a smooth, thick paste forms. Transfer the pesto to a bowl. Stir in salt and pepper to taste. Heat through before serving.

   *Vegan option: skip the eggs

Chicken Bone Broth

BUILDING BLOCK BASIC | ⏱ 12 - 24 HRS
largely unattended

🥄 EASY | YIELDS 10 CUPS

Ingredients

1 whole chicken

Water (enough to cover chicken and fill crock pot)

1 tablespoon garlic powder

1 tablespoon turmeric powder

1 tablespoon apple cider vinegar

1 bay leaf

1 gluten-free chicken bouillon cube

Directions:

Rinse chicken and place in crock pot. Cover with water. Add bay leaf, apple cider vinegar, garlic powder, and turmeric powder. Cook on low for 12 to 24 hours. Strain through a colander placed over a large pot or bowl to catch the broth. Add chicken bouillon cube to the broth and allow to dissolve. Stir well. Let cool and store in containers in the freezer until ready to use.

Remove the meat from the chicken, and store in containers in the freezer until ready to use. *This can be added to the broth for chicken soup, or it can be used for chicken salad. (Follow recipe for Salmon Salad (page 87), using the shredded chicken instead.)*

Veggie Broth

BUILDING BLOCK BASIC | ⏱ 8 - 12 HRS
largely unattended

🥄 EASY | YIELDS 10-12 CUPS

Ingredients

Veggie scraps from chopping (onion, garlic, celery, carrot, etc)

Water (enough to fill crock pot)

1 tablespoon garlic powder

1 tablespoon turmeric powder

1 bay leaf

1 gluten-free veggie bouillon cube

Directions:

Place veggies in crock pot. Pour water over the veggies until the crock pot is full. Add bay leaf, garlic powder, and turmeric powder. Cook on low for 8-12 hours. Strain veggies through a colander placed over a large pot or bowl. Add bouillon cube to the broth and allow to dissolve. Stir well. Let cool and store in containers in the freezer until ready to use.

Big Batch Beans

BUILDING BLOCK BASIC

 1/2 - 3 HRS
largely unattended

 EASY | YIELDS 8-3/4 CUPS

Ingredients

1 pound dried beans, like chickpeas or black beans (*see lentil and split pea option on opposite page)

Kombu (edible kelp)

2 teaspoons salt

1 teaspoon black pepper

If you don't have time to soak the beans overnight, you can use this quick soak method: Put rinsed beans in a large pot and cover with an inch of water. Place on the stove over high heat and bring to a boil. Boil for 2 minutes, then turn heat off. Put a lid on the pot and allow the beans to soak for two hours. Proceed to the cooking directions below.

Directions:

Rinse the beans and pick through them for stones or debris. Soak overnight or up to 12 hours before cooking. Rinse beans again and put them in a large pot with a piece of kombu, covering with at least an inch of water. Bring beans to a boil, then reduce heat and bring to a simmer. Cover the pot with a lid and cook, undisturbed, for 45 minutes, adding water as needed to keep the level about 1 inch above the beans. Taste a bean to check tenderness. (Keep checking for tenderness every 15 minutes.) Once beans are slightly tender, add the salt and pepper. Once salt and pepper have been added, return the liquid to a gentle simmer and cover. Sample a bean every 10 to 15 minutes to check for doneness. Add more water if necessary, keeping the beans barely submerged. Stop cooking when the beans are as firm or creamy as you like them. (Small beans, such as lentils or split peas, will take as little as 15 minutes more; large beans can take up to an hour or more.) Remove the kombu and adjust the seasoning to taste. Drain beans and reserve the liquid separately. The beans can be used in salads or other dishes where they need to be more firm, or finish all or some of them with one of the ingredients from the list that follows.

To store:

Refrigerate for up to 1 week, keeping the beans and their cooking liquid in an airtight container. Drain off the liquid as needed; it comes in handy when making soup.

Freeze by dividing into individual or meal-size portions, barely covering with cooking liquid, and placing in airtight containers. Be sure to leave an inch of room at the top of the container to allow for expansion when it freezes. Frozen beans can be stored for several months. To thaw, put the frozen beans in the refrigerator overnight or in a pot over low heat.

Big Batch Lentils, Split Peas, or Other Small Beans

Directions:

Follow the directions in the Big Batch Bean recipe, only start checking the beans or peas for doneness after about 15 minutes. Small beans will break down quickly and become soupy. (If you want lentils firm enough for salads or stir-fries, watch them closely, and drain them immediately once they are tender and before they break open.) Drain, reserving the cooking liquid, and run under cold water to stop them from cooking further.

Slow Cooker

Directions:

Follow the directions in the main recipe, but use a slow cooker set on high heat. Start checking the beans after 3 hours, and after that check them every 30 minutes or so. (This method doesn't work with lentils, split-peas, or small beans, as it will turn them into soup!)

Flavoring Ideas for Cooked Grains or Beans

Most likely, you will want to flavor only a portion of grains or beans at a time. It's fun to play around with different seasonings for different meals.

Chopped fresh tomatoes

Leftover cooked veggies, like greens or peppers

Sesame oil

Olive oil

Any vinaigrette

Gluten-free, soy-free Miso, thinned with a little hot water or cooking liquid

Hot sauce

Spice blend, like curry or chili powder

Minced fresh chile, ginger, or garlic

Chopped fresh herbs or crumbled dried herbs

Balsamic, umi plum, coconut, or any white vinegar

Tamari sauce, coconut aminos, or liquid aminos

Big Batch Rice and Grains

Options to choose from include wild rice, brown rice, quinoa, or steel cut oats. This batch can be stored in your fridge for salads, soups, or as single or multiple servings. It can be reheated on the stovetop with a few drops of water and some oil. Freeze in one-meal portions for a few months, then thaw in the fridge overnight before using.

BUILDING BLOCK BASIC	 15 MIN - 1 HR
⎰ EASY	YIELDS 8-1 CUP SERVINGS

Ingredients

3 cups almost any rice or whole grain (about 1 ½ pounds)

2 teaspoons salt, plus more to taste

If you are able to soak the wild rice overnight before cooking, it cooks much faster.

Wild rice is my favorite, because it is a grass, making it a great option for people who are trying to avoid grains

Directions:

First, rinse the rice or grains in a strainer. Then put them in a large pot and add the salt. Cover with about 1 inch of water, but not more. Bring to a boil, then reduce heat to low. Cover and simmer gently, until most of the water is absorbed and the grains are tender. Allow about 15 to 20 minutes for steel-cut oats, 20 to 25 minutes for quinoa, at least 30 minutes for long-grain brown rice, and 1 hour or more for many specialty rices and sturdier grains. Add a very small amount of boiling water if needed to avoid sticking and burning.

As the water is absorbed, small holes will form between the rice or grains. Once this happens, cover the pot and remove it from the heat. If grains are done but some water remains, drain them in a strainer, return them to the pot, and replace the cover. They'll keep warm for about 20 minutes. When ready to serve, fluff the grains gently with a fork. These can be served as is or with flavorings from the list on page 49. Have fun with mixing and matching flavorings!

Cauliflower Rice

This is a great grain-free option. For the simplest option, buy pre-shredded cauliflower rice in the freezer section of the grocery store or in bulk where available.

Follow instructions on the package

BUILDING BLOCK BASIC	25 MIN
🍴 EASY	SERVES 4-6

Ingredients

1 head of cauliflower, riced using the grating attachment on your food processor

2 tablespoons olive oil

¼ cup water

Garlic powder

Salt

Pepper

Directions:

In a medium skillet, heat the olive oil over medium heat. Add the cauliflower and sauté for a couple of minutes. Add the water and cover. Reduce the heat to medium-low and cook for 15 minutes. Remove the lid and continue cooking, stirring occasionally. It is done when the water is absorbed and rice is lightly browned, about 5 minutes. Season to taste with garlic powder, salt, and pepper.

Slow Cooker Potatoes

BUILDING BLOCK BASIC	 **8 - 10 HRS** -slow cooker **30 - 45 MIN** -oven
EASY	SERVES 6-10

Ingredients

6-10 whole white or sweet potatoes, rinsed

Directions:

Place the potatoes in a slow cooker and cook on low for 8 - 10 hours or approximately 30 minutes in the oven. When the potatoes are done, store in an air tight container in the refrigerator until ready to use. These keep for approximately 5 days.

Oven option:

Preheat oven to 425 degrees, and bake potatoes for 30-45 minutes or until fork-tender.

These can be used for Build-Your-Own Smashed and Loaded Mashed Potatoes (page 80), Shawarma (page 116), Burger Bowls (page118), Home Fries (page 55), Steak Fries (page 54), Veggie Hash with Eggs (page 64), soups, etc...

Steak Fries

BUILDING BLOCK BASIC | 45 MIN

EASY | SERVES 2-6

Ingredients

1 - 3 white or sweet Slow Cooker Potatoes
(page 52)

2 - 4 tablespoons olive oil

Salt

Pepper

Garlic salt

Cayenne pepper (optional)

Directions:

Preheat oven to 425 degrees.

Slice potatoes into steak fries and place evenly on parchment paper-lined baking sheet, not overlapping. Drizzle with olive oil, then bake for 20 minutes. Turn and continue baking for 20 - 30 minutes to desired crispiness. Season with salt, pepper, garlic powder, and cayenne pepper to taste.

Home Fries

BUILDING BLOCK BASIC | 30 MIN

EASY | SERVES 2-6

Ingredients

1-3 white or sweet Slow Cooker Potatoes
(page 52), diced in half inch dice

¼ cup olive oil

Salt

Pepper

Garlic salt

Directions:

In large cast-iron skillet, heat olive oil over medium heat. Add diced potatoes and simmer, stirring occasionally, for about 20 minutes until crispy. Drain on paper towels and season to taste with salt, pepper, and garlic salt.

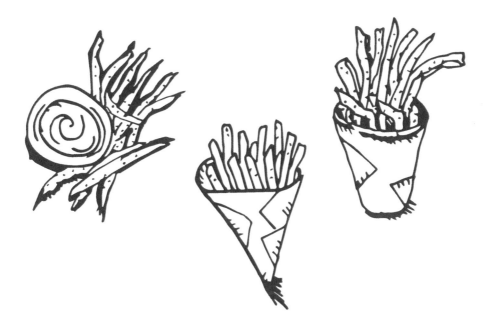

Uncle Tom's Brussels Sprouts

Inspired by my husband's Uncle Tom. It is an annual tradition for him to make these at Thanksgiving. We added the hot sauce because we love heat on our food.

BUILDING BLOCK BASIC **20 MIN**

EASY | SERVES 4-6

Ingredients

1 pound Brussels sprouts, trimmed and halved

2 cloves garlic, minced

¼ cup olive oil

Sea salt

Pepper

Frank's® hot sauce

Directions:

Preheat oven to 500 degrees.

Pour olive oil into a large, oven-safe skillet (I prefer cast-iron). Place Brussels sprouts flat-side down in the skillet. Cook on stovetop over medium-high heat for 5-10 minutes, until browned and crispy. Don't stir. Add garlic, then remove from heat and transfer to the oven. Bake for 5 minutes. Season with salt and pepper to taste. Top with Frank's® hot sauce and enjoy!

Roasted Cauliflower with Sesame Seeds

BUILDING BLOCK BASIC

 35 MIN

EASY | SERVES 4

Ingredients

1 head cauliflower, trimmed and cut into 8 wedges

6 tablespoons extra virgin olive oil

Sea salt and ground pepper

1 tablespoon coconut vinegar

1 teaspoon coconut sugar

2 tablespoons capers; rinsed, drained, and roughly chopped

⅛ cup toasted sesame seeds

2 tablespoons chopped fresh parsley leaves

Directions:

Place oven rack in middle position. Put a heavy-rimmed baking sheet on the rack, and preheat oven to 500 degrees.

Put cauliflower and 3 tablespoons olive oil in large mixing bowl and toss to coat. Generously season with salt and pepper. Remove the baking sheet from the oven, using oven mitts. Place the cauliflower pieces on the baking sheet and return to the oven. Roast until cauliflower is tender and deeply browned, 20 - 30 minutes total. Flip the cauliflower with a thin spatula halfway through.

While the cauliflower is roasting, combine the remaining 3 tablespoons of olive oil, vinegar, coconut sugar, capers, sesame seeds, and parsley in a medium bowl and season with salt and pepper. Transfer roasted cauliflower to serving platter and spoon dressing on top. Serve immediately.

Breakfast Recipes

Avocado Toast

BREAKFAST 5 MIN

 EASY | SERVES 2-6

Ingredients

2-6 slices Hearty Seed Bread, toasted (recipe on page 37)

Eggs, over easy (optional)

1-2 avocados, sliced

Olive oil or ghee

Salt

Pepper

Oregano

Directions:

Put a little ghee or olive oil on the bread, then top with avocado and over-easy eggs. Sprinkle with salt, pepper, and oregano to taste.

For over-easy eggs*: heat an omelet pan over medium heat. Place 2 tablespoons ghee in the pan. Once the ghee stops sizzling, add 2 eggs. Cover and cook for 2 - 4 minutes, until the top of the eggs becomes opaque. Check eggs about once a minute to make sure they don't overcook.

  *Vegan option: serve without egg

Veggie Hash with Eggs

Choose veggies that you already have in your refrigerator, and be creative, to make an easy Sunday brunch. Our family loves adding Uncle Tom's Brussels Sprouts to this recipe. (page 57)

BREAKFAST | **30 MIN**

EASY | SERVES 2-4

Ingredients

¼ cup olive oil, plus more for drizzling

1-2 Slow Cooker Potatoes (recipe on page 52), diced

1 onion, diced

2 cups broccoli, diced

1 cup bell or mini peppers

1-2 cloves garlic, minced

4-8 eggs, whisked

Salt and pepper

Directions:

Preheat oven to 450 degrees.

Add olive oil to a large cast-iron skillet over medium heat. Add the diced potatoes, onion, and peppers. Sauté for approximately 20 minutes, turning often to brown evenly. In the meantime, place the broccoli and diced pepper on a baking sheet lined with parchment paper. Drizzle with olive oil. Place in preheated oven and roast for 20 minutes.

When the potatoes and broccoli are both slightly browned and crispy, add the garlic to the potatoes and sauté for about 30 seconds. Add the roasted broccoli to the skillet, and move the veggies to one side of the skillet. Make sure the skillet is coated with a little oil or butter, then add the eggs to the cleared off area. Scramble the eggs, then turn off the heat and mix the veggies and eggs together. Serve immediately.

*Vegan option: skip the eggs

Bacon & Egg "Cupcakes"

BREAKFAST	25 MIN
EASY	SERVES 6

Ingredients

Coconut oil or butter for greasing

6 strips bacon

6 eggs

Chopped herbs (optional)

Salt and pepper to taste

Directions:

Preheat oven to 400 degrees.

Lightly grease a 6-cup muffin pan. Line the edge of each muffin cup with bacon strips. Place pan in the oven for 10 minutes, then take out to add the eggs. Crack 1 egg into each muffin cup, then sprinkle with herbs, salt and pepper. Bake for 15 minutes or until the egg whites are set. Cool for 2 minutes before using a knife or spoon to gently remove the cupcakes from the pan. Serve hot or warm. (Store leftovers in the fridge and reheat in oven.)

  Make it vegetarian: Add sauteed veggies to bottom of the muffin cups, instead of bacon, then crack egg over the veggies and bake for 15 minutes

Slow Cooker Oatmeal

BREAKFAST **4-8 HRS**
largely unattended

EASY | SERVES 6

Ingredients

1 ½ cups steel-cut oats

6 cups almond or coconut beverage

⅓ cup maple syrup or honey

1 teaspoon vanilla powder

1 teaspoon cinnamon

1/8 teaspoon sea salt

1 cup frozen blueberries

¼ cup coconut yogurt (optional)

Directions:

Place all ingredients (except berries and yogurt) in a slow cooker and cook on low for 8 hours (or on high for 4 hours). Add blueberries for the last half hour. Stir and enjoy! Top with coconut yogurt.

Fruity Nut Spread

BREAKFAST | **5 MIN**

EASY | 2 CUPS

Ingredients

1 cup macadamia nuts

2 cups fresh or frozen blueberries

1 tablespoon fresh lemon juice

Directions:

Place nuts in a food processor and pulse until coarsely chopped. Add blueberries and lemon juice, then process until creamy and smooth. (You may need to scrape the sides of the food processor with a spatula a couple of times).

Spread on Hearty Seed Bread (page 37), gluten-free toast, waffles, or pancakes. Serve right away or store in a sealed container and refrigerate up to 3 days.

Other combos: apple/walnut, pear/pecan, apricot/pistachio, almond/peaches, strawberry/pine nut, banana/peanut, mango/cashew

Kale Smoothie

BREAKFAST | **5 MIN**

EASY | SERVES 1

Ingredients

¼ cup coconut yogurt

2 cups packed kale

½ - 1 cup coconut milk

¼ cup cashew butter

1 tablespoon chia seeds

1 teaspoon maca powder

½ frozen banana

¼ teaspoon vanilla powder

Directions:

Place all ingredients in blender and blend until smooth.

Granola

This recipe is inspired by my Grandma Van Meter. The smell of freshly baked granola brings back wonderful memories of my grandmother in the kitchen.

BREAKFAST	⊙ **35 MIN**
🥄 EASY	YIELDS 1 LARGE JAR

Ingredients

2 cups gluten-free oats

1 heaped cup mixed nuts (brazil nuts, almonds, cashews, pecans, hazelnuts)

¼ cup mixed seeds (sunflower, pumpkin, sesame, poppy)

¾ cup unsweetened, shredded coconut

1 teaspoon ground cinnamon

1 teaspoon ground cardamom

5 tablespoons melted honey

5 tablespoons melted coconut oil

Directions:

Preheat the oven to 350 degrees.

Place all of the dry ingredients on a cookie sheet. Mix together and spread evenly over the cookie sheet. Drizzle with melted honey and coconut oil and stir again. Bake for 25 to 30 minutes, stirring every 5 or so minutes. Let it cool and enjoy!

 *Vegan option: use Agave nectar in place of honey

Lunch Recipes

Lentil Salad

This salad is loaded with flavor and texture...a favorite go-to for me!

LUNCH	15 MIN
⅋ EASY	SERVES 4

Ingredients

1 tablespoon Dijon or other good quality mustard

2 tablespoons wine or sherry vinegar

4 tablespoons olive oil

2 tablespoons water

1 teaspoon salt, plus more to taste

Black pepper to taste

4 cups canned or big batch lentils, or any other bean, drained

3 large ripe tomatoes, chopped

1 large cucumber, peeled, seeded, and chopped

1 cup chopped carrots or radishes

1 cup chopped celery or fennel

½ cup chopped red onion

1/4 cup chopped fresh parsley or dill

Directions:

Place the mustard, vinegar, oil, salt, 2 tablespoons water, and a pinch of pepper in a large bowl and whisk until combined. Add all of the remaining ingredients to the bowl, and toss to coat with the dressing. Adjust the seasoning to taste, and serve. (This salad can be made ahead of time: just combine everything, excluding the tomatoes and parsley, but don't toss: cover and refrigerate for up to a day. Allow ingredients to come back to room temperature, and toss before serving.)

Build-Your-Own Smashed and Loaded Sweet Potato

This is an easy meal, loaded with flavor and fun for the whole family. Use leftovers if you wish, and everyone can add toppings of choice to their own.

LUNCH	⏱ 5 MIN
🥄 EASY	SERVES 4-6

Ingredients

4 - 6 large sweet potatoes, baked or cooked in slow cooker*

2 tablespoons olive oil

1 teaspoon salt, plus more to taste

Black pepper to taste

Ingredients from following list, alone or in combination

Directions:

Allow potatoes to cool, then cut them in half and mash them with a fork or potato masher; sprinkle with salt and pepper and drizzle with olive oil. Top with ingredients of your choice from the list below (or be creative with what you have on hand) and serve. It's fun to set out different toppings and let everyone choose their favorites.

*Use your Slow Cooker Potatoes (page 52) that are prepped for the week. If using pre-made potatoes that are in your fridge, warm in a 350 degree oven for 20 - 30 minutes before using.

Sweet and Savory
Toppings

Up to 4 cups of any cooked greens

1 cup roasted red bell peppers

Up to ½ cup gluten-free, soy-free miso paste

2 cups peas or fava beans (frozen are fine)

1 tablespoon ginger

½ to 1 cup chopped fresh herbs like parsley, basil, or cilantro

Red chile flakes, paprika, or cayenne to taste

Up to ¾ cup traditional pesto

Hot sauce

Tahini sauce

Herb puree

Tamari sauce to taste

Balsamic vinegar to taste

Maple syrup to taste

½ cup chopped olives

½ cup chopped nuts like peanuts, pecans, or hazelnuts

2 cups black beans, cannelloni, or chickpeas

2 tablespoons chopped chipotle in adobo

1 head roasted garlic

1 tablespoon horseradish

Mason Jar Salad

This easy salad can be prepped at the beginning of the week so lunches are ready to grab as you run out the door. This is a go-to for me on days that I am working outside the home.

LUNCH	⟨·⟩ 5 MIN
⚲ EASY	YIELDS 1 QUART

Ingredients

FOR THE DRESSING (ADD TO EACH JAR):

2 tablespoons olive oil

1 tablespoon vinegar (apple cider, balsamic, or coconut) or lemon juice

Herbs, to taste

Dijon mustard, to taste

Vegenaise®, to taste (optional)

Salt and pepper, to taste

FOR THE SALAD:

Mix of raw and cooked vegetables

Nuts & seeds, such as pumpkin seeds, sunflower seeds, hemp seeds, sesame seeds

Cooked or canned beans, such as: black beans, garbanzo, lentils, adzuki beans

Cooked grains or rice, such a brown rice or quinoa

Sauerkraut

Olives

Any salad ingredients you have on hand

Salad greens

Directions:

Add olive oil to the bottom of the jar along with vinegar or lemon juice. Season with herbs, dijon mustard, Vegenaise®, salt, and pepper to taste.

Next, add any firm chopped vegetables you want to include in your salad. These may include carrots, broccoli, peppers, fennel, sauerkraut, or olives. You can be creative with whatever you have on hand.

Add beans, grains, and/or nuts and seeds.

If you want, you can add in other proteins, such as chicken, tuna, Tu-Not Salad (page 85), salmon, or Salmon Salad (page87), hard-boiled egg, etc. Be creative with any leftovers you may have in your fridge. When making salads ahead to keep in your refrigerator, add protein to the top of the jar on the day you will be eating, to prevent the protein from spoiling.

Fill the rest of the jar with salad greens or sprouts. Tear the lettuce into bite-size pieces, and pack jar to the top.

Top the jar with a lid and refrigerate for up to 5 days. Any proteins, soft fruits or vegetables should be added to the top of the jar the morning you plan to eat your salad.

When ready to eat, shake the jar, then empty the contents into your bowl. This will distribute the dressing evenly.

Tu-Not Salad

LUNCH | **10 MIN**

¶ EASY | SERVES 4

Ingredients

1 (15.5 ounce) can garbanzo beans or 2 cups Big Batch Garbanzo Beans (page 48)

¼ cup Vegenaise® (egg-free, gluten-free mayonnaise)

1 ½ tablespoons ume plum vinegar

2 teaspoons whole celery seeds

¼ cup chopped celery, about 1 rib

2 tablespoons sliced scallions, about 2 scallions

Pinch cayenne pepper, optional

Sea salt and ground black pepper

Directions:

Place garbanzo beans in bowl of food processor. Pulse 2-3 times to roughly chop. Add all the remaining ingredients, except celery. Pulse 2-3 more times to incorporate, then place in a bowl. Stir in the celery. Spread generously on Hearty Seed Bread (page 37), Paleo "Tortilla" Wrap (page 35) with avocado, pickle, and lettuce, or use in a green or Mason Jar Salad (page 82).

Salmon Salad

Choose wild-caught salmon and avoid factory-farmed salmon for better quality and health benefits.

LUNCH

 10 MIN

EASY

SERVES 2

Ingredients

1 (6 ounce) can wild-caught salmon

¼ cup Vegenaise®

Juice of 1/2 lemon

¼ cup chopped onion

¼ cup chopped celery

1 teaspoon dill weed

1 tablespoon finely chopped jalapeño (optional)

Salt and pepper to taste

Directions:

Mix all ingredients together. This can be refrigerated for up to 3 days.

Serve on a Paleo Tortilla Wrap (page 34) or on Hearty Seed Bread (page 37) with avocado, pickle, and lettuce. This can also be used in a Mason Jar Salad (page 82), or on a bed of greens with other vegetables. Dress salad with a drizzle of olive oil (about 2 tablespoons), 2 teaspoons vinegar of choice or lemon, garlic powder, salt, and pepper.

Pulled Pork Wrap

LUNCH	15 MIN
🥄 EASY	YIELDS 6 WRAPS

Ingredients

6 Paleo "Tortilla" Wraps (page 35)

1 cup shredded pork from Slow Cooker Pork Shoulder (page 108)

½ cup reserved juices from Slow Cooker Pork Shoulder

6 slices prosciutto or 12 slices bacon, cooked

12 dill pickle slices

FOR DIJON AIOLI:

¼ cup Vegenaise®

1 tablespoon plus 1 teaspoon Dijon mustard

1 teaspoon lemon juice

¼ teaspoon ground cumin

⅛ teaspoon ground dried oregano

Directions:

Thaw the wraps, if frozen, by letting them sit at room temperature for 30 minutes.

Reheat the shredded pork and juices in a pan over medium heat until warmed through. While pork is heating, make the Dijon aioli. Whisk together all of the ingredients in a small bowl.

Heat a skillet over medium-high heat. Assemble each wrap by placing a spoonful of shredded pork, a slice of prosciutto or 2 slices cooked bacon, 2 pickle slices, and a tablespoon of the Dijon Aioli on half of the wrap. Fold in half, then brown on the skillet for about 2 minutes per side.

* Vegan option: omit the pork and procuitto and add in sliced cucumber, tomato, alfalfa sprouts & avocado

Dinner Recipes

Lentil Soup

DINNER | ⏱ 1 HR

🥄 EASY | SERVES 6-8

Ingredients

10 cups water

3 cups lentils, rinsed and picked through

1 onion, diced

1 cup celery, diced

1 head garlic

4-5 tablespoons olive oil

1 ½ cups carrots, roughly chopped

1 ½ cups broccoli, cut into bite-sized pieces

1 cup potato, boiled for 5 minutes and diced (or use Slow Cooker Potatoes from page 52, if on hand)

Sea salt

Pepper

1 tablespoon oregano

Directions:

Preheat oven to 425 degrees.

Cut the top off of the head of garlic. Place on a piece of foil, drizzle with about a tablespoon of olive oil, and sprinkle with a little sea salt. Close the foil loosely, and place the garlic in the oven. Roast for about 45 minutes or until fragrant.

In a small skillet, add 2 tablespoons of olive oil and turn to medium heat, then add the onions and celery. Sauté onion and celery in large pot until browned. Once browned add the water and lentils.

Bring water and lentils to a boil in a large pot. Check the tenderness of a lentil after about 10 minutes. When slightly softened, add a tablespoon of sea salt. Continue to boil until tender, but not falling apart. Reduce heat to low.

When the garlic has about 30 minutes left, place parchment paper on a baking sheet, and then evenly distribute the carrots, broccoli, and potatoes on it. Drizzle with olive oil and sprinkle with a little sea salt. Roast for 20 - 30 minutes, until lightly browned and slightly crispy.

Allow the head of garlic to cool while adding all of the other vegetables into the pot of lentils and water. Then place the cooled, peeled garlic cloves in a blender. Ladle about 4 cups of the soup into the blender and allow to cool for a few minutes before blending. Blend until creamy and pour back into the soup pot. Add oregano and pepper to taste.

Chicken Soup

Inspired by my husband's grandmother, Omi.
She was always making chicken soup to bring healing to others.

DINNER	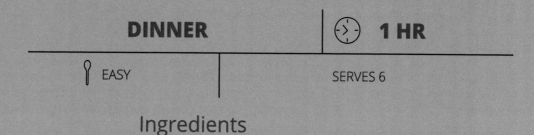 1 HR
⌻ EASY	SERVES 6

Ingredients

8 cups Chicken Bone Broth (page 46)

1 head garlic

Olive oil

4 cups roughly chopped veggies for roasting (see opposite page)

1 onion, diced

1 cup chopped celery

2 cups cooked wild rice, optional

2 cups shredded chicken from broth recipe

Sea salt

Pepper

Chopped or dried herbs, such as parsley or oregano

Directions:

Preheat oven to 425 degrees.

Cut the top off of the head of garlic, leaving the cloves connected to the base. Place the head of garlic in foil and drizzle a little olive oil over it. Close loosely and place in preheated oven for 45 minutes to an hour, until fragrant. When done, allow garlic to cool, and then peel the cloves.

Spread veggies evenly on a baking sheet lined with parchment paper. Drizzle with olive oil and sprinkle with salt to taste. Place in oven and roast for 20 minutes or until lightly browned.

Heat a medium-sized skillet over medium heat. Add 2 tablespoons of olive oil. When warm, add onions and chopped celery. Sauté until soft and lightly browned, 10 - 15 minutes.

Heat the chicken broth, minus 1 cup, in a large pot. Place peeled garlic cloves in a blender along along with 1 cup of cooled chicken broth. Blend until smooth. Add to the broth in the pot with shredded chicken, roasted veggies, cabbage, sautééd onion, and celery. Add salt, pepper, and chopped herbs to taste.

VEGGIE OPTIONS FOR ROASTING

Carrots   Brussels sprouts

Potatoes   Fennel

Broccoli   Parsnips

Buddha Bowl
with Tahini Dressing

DINNER	45 MIN
MEDIUM	SERVES 4-6

Ingredients

1 cup short-grain brown or wild rice, rinsed (Or use prepared rice from making Big Batch Rice (page 50) at the beginning of the week)

2 cups water or vegetable broth (page 46)

Pinch of sea salt

4 tablespoons extra-virgin olive oil

Freshly ground pepper, to taste

2 cups peeled, cubed butternut or kabocha squash

1 medium yellow onion, thinly sliced

6 cups kale, washed, ribs discarded, and leaves chopped

FOR THE DRESSING:

1 teaspoon grated ginger

¼ cup tahini

1 ½ teaspoons honey

1 ½ teaspoons sea salt

¾ cup hot water

Juice of one lemon

ADDITIONAL TOPPINGS:

½ cup toasted walnuts or pumpkin seeds

1 avocado, peeled and diced

Directions:

Preheat the oven to 425 degrees.

Combine the rice, water, and salt in a small pot and bring to a boil. Reduce the heat, cover and simmer for approximately 40 minutes. When water is absorbed, remove from the heat and fluff with a fork. Cover and let rest for another 5 minutes.

*Paleo option: use cauliflower rice (page 51)
*Vegan option: use agave nectar in place of honey

Place squash on a baking sheet lined with parchment paper. Drizzle 2 tablespoons of olive oil over the squash, add salt and pepper to taste. Roast for 20-25 minutes, until lightly browned and fork tender.

Place large sauté pan over medium heat and add 2 tablespoons oil. Add the onions and spread them out evenly in the pan. Allow the onions to rest until they start to brown; stir and reduce the heat to low. Let the onions caramelize for 15 minutes, or until they are soft and brown. Remove the onions from the pan and set aside.

Sauté the kale with a pinch of salt until it turns bright green and softens slightly. Add the onions and stir to combine.

In a blender, combine tahini, lemon, ginger, honey, and 1/2 teaspoon salt. Blend, adding a little bit of water at a time until you reach a smooth and pourable consistency.

Put 1/2 cup rice in the bottom of each bowl. Top with caramelized onions, squash, and kale. Place some diced avocado and toasted nuts on top. Drizzle tahini sauce over the prepared bowls.

For added protein, you can serve chicken or black beans with this.

Mucho Bowl

DINNER | 30 MIN

EASY | SERVES 4

Ingredients

2 cups prepared rice from Big Batch Grains (page 50) or Cauliflower Rice (page 51)

4 cups prepared black beans from Big Batch Beans (page 48)

1 onion, carmelized

2 Poblano or Bell peppers, sautéed

½ teaspoon coriander

1 teaspoon cumin

¼ teaspoon garlic powder

Salt and pepper to taste

Salsa

"Queso" Cashew Sauce (page 43)

Spicy Guacamole (page 150)

Toasted pumpkin seeds

1/4 cup cilantro leaves, chopped

Directions:

Warm leftover rice on the stove in a pan with water covering the bottom, and place a lid on top to warm through.

Heat a skillet over medium heat with 1 tablespoon olive oil. Add the onion and simmer without stirring for about 5 minutes. Continue simmering for another 10 minutes, stirring occasionally. They should get crispy and almost burnt.

Place prepared black beans in a saucepan, adding coriander, cumin, garlic powder, salt, and pepper. Bring to a simmer. Cover and warm through for about 5 minutes.

In individual bowls, add ½ cup warmed rice and 1 cup beans. Top with salsa, guacamole, toasted pumpkin seeds, cilantro, and meat of choice*, if using.

This is good with Black Bean Pesto (page 45) as an alternative to whole black beans if you have some on hand.

*Meat option: try serving with Tomatillo Chicken (page 103), Tostada meat (page 104) or Slow Cooker Pork (page 108)
*Paleo option: use Cauliflower Rice page 51

Veggie Stir-Fry

DINNER | ⏱ 30 MIN

EASY | SERVES 2-4

Ingredients

Prepped rice from the Big Batch Rice or Grains recipe (page 50), or Cauliflower Rice (page 51)

2 tablespoons olive oil

1 cup chopped onions

1 cup chopped carrots

1 tablespoon minced ginger

1 tablespoon minced garlic

1 cup chopped broccoli

1 cup chopped zucchini

1 cup snow peas

Protein of choice (beans, chicken, or Slow Cooker Pork Shoulder page 108)

¼ cup chopped scallions

Salt and pepper to taste

CONDIMENTS:

I keep all of these on hand and set them out so each person can choose what they want on their own stir fry.

Tamari sauce

Coconut aminos

Gluten-free, soy-free miso

Sriracha hot chili sauce

Ume plum vinegar

Toasted sesame seeds

Toasted almond slices

Directions:

In a large sauté skillet, warm the olive oil over medium heat. Add the onions and spread evenly over the skillet. When the onions start to brown, stir and let them caramelize. Remove the onions from the skillet and set aside in a bowl. Sauté carrots and broccoli for about 5 minutes, then add the zucchini and peas. Sauté until slightly brown and crispy. Remove the vegetables from the pan and add to the onions. In the same skillet, add 2 tablespoons water and prepared rice. Warm through, then remove from skillet and place in individual serving bowls. Top with the sautéed vegetables and scallions. Add condiments of choice. Season with salt and pepper to taste.

*Paleo option: use Cauliflower Rice page 51

Tomatillo Chicken

DINNER

 3 HRS -stove top
8 HRS -slow cooker

EASY

SERVES 4

Ingredients

1 tablespoon ghee or coconut oil

8 chicken thighs, bone-in and skin on

Sea salt and black pepper

2 cloves garlic, minced

2 teaspoons ground cumin

2 teaspoons ground coriander

2 cups store-bought tomatillo salsa, divided

Directions:

Place a heavy-bottomed pot or dutch oven over medium-high heat and add ghee.

Generously season the chicken with salt and pepper. In a small bowl, combine the garlic, cumin, and coriander. Rub the seasoning all over the chicken. Brown chicken on all sides, about 2 minutes per side. You may need to do this in batches.

If using a slow cooker, pour 1 cup salsa into the slow cooker and lay the browned thighs on top. Cook on low, covered, for 8 hours.

If using the stovetop, pour 1 cup of salsa over the browned chicken thighs. Cover and simmer over medium-low heat for 3 hours. Add a little water if the salsa starts to dry out to keep the chicken from burning or sticking to the pot.

Serve chicken with the remaining cup of salsa, along with your favorite toppings.

Use in the Buddha Bowl (page 96), Mucho Bowl (page 99) , Veggie stir-fry (page 100), and Build Your Own Pizza (page 110).

Leftovers store nicely in the freezer and can be used when you are in a rush.

Tostadas

These are a favorite of mine when serving a crowd. This recipe was passed down from my mother-in-law, who taught me so much about being a good hostess.

DINNER	🕐 **3.5 HOURS** largely unattended
🍴 MEDIUM	SERVES 6

Ingredients

FOR THE SAUCE:

3 tablespoons olive oil

1 onion, diced

3 cloves garlic, minced

16 oz enchilada sauce

1 ½ pounds grass-fed beef stew meat, optional

1 can diced green chiles

Directions:

Heat the olive oil in a large skillet over medium heat. Add the onions and garlic along with the stew meat. Brown the meat evenly, then add enchilada sauce and green chiles and bring to a simmer. Lower heat to medium-low and simmer for 3 hours, checking every ½ hour that it isn't drying out.

FOR THE SHELLS:

This is where I use sprouted corn tortillas. We have also found quinoa tortillas that are made locally, and they work well too.

12 sprouted corn tortillas (or 2-3 for each person)

Olive oil

Sea salt

Directions:

Preheat the oven to 500 degrees.

Brush olive oil over both sides of each tortilla and lay them flat on baking sheets. Place in the preheated oven for 3 minutes, check them, and add 1 minute at a time until brown and crispy. Watch the tortillas closely so they don't burn. Remove from the oven, and sprinkle with sea salt. Allow to cool before serving.

FOR THE LAYER TOPPINGS OF YOUR CHOICE:

Canned refried beans, Big Batch Black Beans (page 48), or Black Bean Pesto (page 45)

Tostada meat, or meatless sauce

Spicy Guacamole (page 150)

Shredded lettuce

Chopped tomatoes

Diced or pickled jalapenos

Salsa

Hot sauce

"Queso" Cashew Sauce (page 43)

*Vegan option, sauté the onion and garlic in the olive oil for about 5 minutes, until translucent. Add enchilada sauce and green chiles, and simmer for about 10 minutes over low heat. Other veggies can be added in with the onions and garlic, if you are feeling creative. Serve with beans instead of meat.

*Paleo option: serve over greens or cauliflower rice pg 51, instead of tortillas

Spaghetti
with Spaghetti Squash

DINNER	⏲ 30 MIN
🥄 EASY	SERVES 6

Ingredients

FOR THE SQUASH:

Olive oil for drizzling

Salt and pepper

1 large spaghetti squash, seeded and sliced in half the long way, then cut into 1 inch "half moons"

FOR THE SAUCE:

6 tablespoons olive oil

1 onion, diced

3 cloves garlic, minced

1 pound grass-fed ground beef, optional

1 cup mushrooms, sliced

1 cup mini peppers, sliced

28 oz. jar marinara

32 ounce tomato puree

salt & pepper to taste

1 tablespoon oregano

Directions:

Preheat the oven to 450 degrees.

Line a baking sheet with parchment paper. Place the squash "moons" evenly on baking sheet so they don't overlap. Drizzle olive oil over the slices and sprinkle with salt and a little pepper.

Bake for about 20 minutes. then flip and bake for 10 - 20 minutes longer, until lightly browned. Once the squash is in the oven, start making the sauce.

Warm 4 tablespoons olive oil in large skillet over medium heat. Add onions and peppers, and sauté for about 5-7 minutes, until soft. Add ground beef, if using, and brown through. In a separate skillet, heat the remaining 2 tablespoons of olive oil, and brown mushrooms evenly on both sides, approximately 2 minutes per side (you might have to do this in a couple of batches so the mushrooms aren't crowded in the pan). Remove mushrooms from the heat, then add the mushrooms and garlic to the onions and peppers. Pour the marinara sauce and tomato sauce into the skillet with the vegetables and meat. Let simmer for 20 minutes, then turn to low until squash is done. shred the squash with two forks and top with sauce.

  *Vegan option: I use roasted veggies: broccoli, bell peppers, carrots, etc.

Slow Cooker Pork Shoulder

DINNER	**8 HRS** largely unattended
⸙ EASY	SERVES 8-10

Ingredients

1 tablespoon bacon fat or ghee

5 pounds boneless pork shoulder roast, cut into 4 large chunks

Sea salt and cracked black pepper

6 ounces pancetta, diced

2 small yellow onions, diced

5 cloves garlic, minced

1 ½ teaspoons fennel seeds

¾ cup dry red wine

1 cup Chicken Bone Broth (page46)

1 pound carrots, peeled and cut into 3 inch pieces

Directions:

Melt the bacon fat or ghee in a deep skillet over medium-high heat. Season the pork shoulder pieces generously with salt and pepper on all sides. Brown the pieces on all sides in batches, then place in the slow cooker. Using the same skillet that you used to brown the pork, sauté the pancetta, onions, garlic, and fennel seeds over medium heat for about 5-7 minutes. Put this mixture over the pork. While the pan is still hot, pour in the wine and stir, scraping up browned bits on the bottom of the pan. Pour this and the chicken broth into the slow cooker. Cover and cook on low for 8 hours, adding the carrots during the last 2 hours of cooking.

To serve:
Pull the pork apart with 2 forks. Serve with a bit of the sauce ladled over the top.

Use in : Build Your Own Smashed and Loaded Sweet Potato (page 80), Pulled Pork Wrap (page 88), Buddha Bowl (page 96), Veggie Stir-fry (page 100), and Build Your Own Pizza (page 110).

Store leftovers in the freezer in meal-sized portions to use for last-minute meals.

Build-Your-Own
Pizza

This is a family favorite. We have come to enjoy this more than the carry-out pizza we used to get. Everyone can be creative with their own toppings, and it's also a great way to spend time with the family. This is a fun meal to make when serving only one person or a crowd.

DINNER	**30 MIN**
EASY	SERVES 1-10

Ingredients

1 - 10 gluten-free tortillas, or Flatbread Pizza Crust, made ahead (page39)

Choose from these toppings: Be creative. (The options are endless!)

Tomato Pizza Sauce (page 38)	Mushrooms	Prosciutto
Barbecue sauce	Slow Cooker Pork Shoulder (page 108)	Sliced zucchini
Pesto	Tomatillo Chicken (page 103)	Basil Pesto (page 42)
Pepperoni slices	Tomato slices	Black Bean Pesto (page 45)
Shredded chicken	Kalamata olives	Poblano peppers
Pine nuts	Caramelized onions	Bell peppers
Onion slices	Arugula	Parmesan cheese
		Vegan cheese

We make our pizzas without cheese or with a little bit of grated parmesan, nutritional yeast, or a nut-based cheese.

Directions:

Set toppings out in bowls on the counter. Preheat oven to 500 degrees.

Place tortillas or pizza crusts on baking sheets. Have everyone put the toppings of their choice on their tortilla or crust. Bake for 5 - 10 minutes. Tortillas will bake quicker, so check after 5 minutes and add 1 minute at a time if needed.

*Vegan or paleo options (depending on crust and topping choices)

Vegan Mac & Cheese
with Roasted Veggies

This is a favorite in our house. It helps to get all of the ingredients prepped and measured out before starting, since there are so many steps. I also like to have an assistant on hand for chopping and keeping up on dishes as I cook!

DINNER	⏱ 1 HR
▼▼▼ ADVANCED	SERVES 4

Ingredients

1 head garlic

12 ounces lentil or chickpea pasta

4 tablespoons olive oil, plus more for drizzling

4 cloves garlic, minced

4 ½ tablespoons arrowroot starch

2 cups unsweetened almond beverage, plus more as needed

¼ teaspoon sea salt

¼ teaspoon pepper

5 tablespoons nutritional yeast

½ cup cashew cheese (see opposite page), plus more for serving

2-4 cups vegetables, cut into bite-size pieces

1 onion, diced for caramelizing

Directions:

Preheat oven to 425 degrees.

Cut off the top of a head of garlic. Drizzle with olive oil and sprinkle with salt. Place in foil, and loosely wrap. Place directly on oven rack and bake for about 45 minutes, until garlic is fragrant and the bulb is golden. Remove from the oven and let cool.

Make the Cashew Cheese (see below).

Prepare a baking sheet by lining it with parchment paper. Place vegetables on the baking sheet; drizzle with olive oil and sprinkle with a little salt. Put in the oven along with the garlic that is roasting. Roast the vegetables for 20 minutes, until lightly browned and slightly crispy.

Meanwhile, heat a medium-size skillet over medium heat with 1 tablespoon olive oil. Add the onions and simmer without stirring for about 5 minutes. Stir and continue simmering for another 10 minutes, stirring occasionally. They should get crispy and almost burnt.

When there are about 30 minutes left for the garlic to roast, put 10 cups of water and a generous pinch of salt into a large pot and bring to a boil. Once the water is boiling, add the pasta and cook according to the package directions. Drain and set aside.

After you have removed the garlic and roasted veggies from the oven, set the oven to broil and allow to preheat. Allow the garlic to cool, and then peel the cloves and set aside.

Heat a large dutch oven or oven-safe skillet over medium heat. Add olive oil and minced garlic. Stir for 30 seconds, then add the arrowroot powder. Whisk for about a minute. Add the almond beverage slowly while continuing to whisk. Cook for about 2 more minutes, stirring frequently. The mixture may be clumpy, but that's okay, since it will be blended.

Allow the milk mixture to cool for a couple of minutes, then put it into a blender. Add the peeled roasted garlic cloves, salt, pepper, nutritional yeast, and cashew cheese. Blend on high until smooth and creamy. Return sauce to the dutch oven and heat for another couple of minutes. It will continue to thicken, so add more milk, 1 tablespoon at a time, if needed to achieve desired consistency. Turn off heat. Add the drained pasta, caramelized onions, and roasted vegetables to the cheese mixture. Stir to incorporate. Sprinkle some of the remaining cashew cheese over the top. Place the dutch oven under the broiler for 2 - 3 minutes to make the top crispy. Watch carefully to make sure the top doesn't burn.

Be creative with the veggies you add. Another favorite of ours is to add Uncle Tom's Brussels Sprouts (page 57)

Cashew Cheese

¾ cup raw cashews
3 tablespoons nutritional yeast

¾ teaspoon sea salt
¼ teaspoon garlic powder

Directions:

Place ingredients in a food processor. Process to a fine meal consistency. Store in fridge.

Potato and Protein Bowls

Shawarma, page 116

Shawarma
with Chicken or Chickpeas

Best on home fries using white potatoes (see Slow Cooker Potatoes recipe on page 52)

BOWLS	30 MIN
MEDIUM	SERVES 4

Ingredients

FOR THE CHICKEN VERSION:

1 tablespoon extra-virgin olive oil

4 boneless, skinless chicken thighs

1/4 cup water

FOR THE CHICKPEA VERSION:

1 tablespoon extra-virgin olive oil

4 cups chickpeas (see Big Batch Beans recipe page 48)

SPICE BLEND:

1 teaspoon salt

½ teaspoon ground cumin

½ teaspoon ground cardamom

¼ teaspoon smoked paprika

¼ teaspoon ground coriander

¼ teaspoon coarse (granulated) garlic powder

⅛ teaspoon black pepper

FOR THE SALAD:

¼ small head red cabbage

1 large carrot

1 tablespoon lemon juice

1 tablespoon extra-virgin olive oil

¼ teaspoon salt

¼ teaspoon ground black pepper

A handful fresh mint leaves

FOR THE TAHINI DRESSING:

1 clove garlic, smashed and peeled

⅓ cup tahini

⅓ cup water

2 tablespoons lemon juice

Pinch salt

Pinch ground black pepper

Directions:

Mix the spice blend ingredients in a small bowl. Rub the spice blend on both sides of the chicken; let rest. Heat the oil in a large, nonstick skillet over medium heat. Place the chicken in the pan and cook it undisturbed for about 5 minutes. Flip the chicken and cook for 2 minutes. Add the water then cover. Reduce heat to medium-low, and simmer until the chicken is cooked through, about 10-15 minutes.

For chickpea version:

Mix the spice blend ingredients in a small bowl. Heat the oil in a large, nonstick skillet over medium heat. Place chickpeas in the skillet and add the spices, stirring to blend. Allow the chickpeas to brown, stirring frequently. Continue to cook until chickpeas are golden brown, then remove them from the heat. Add more olive oil if the chickpeas begin to stick to the pan.

Prep the salad:

Thinly slice the cabbage and carrot, using the slicing blade on your food processor. Combine the vegetables in a large mixing bowl. Add the lemon juice, olive oil, salt, pepper, and mint. Toss and set aside.

Prep the tahini dressing:

With the motor of your food processor running, drop the garlic into the bowl of the food processor. Add the remaining ingredients and process until smooth. (This can be made in a blender if you don't have a food processor. Just add all the ingredients to the blender and blend until smooth).

To serve:

Evenly distribute the potatoes into bowls. Top with cut up chicken pieces or chickpeas, then add the salad and drizzle with tahini dressing.

 *Vegan option: use chickpeas,

 *Paleo option: use chicken

Burger Bowl
Black Bean or Beef Option

Best on Sweet Potato Home Fries (See Slow Cooker Potatoes page 52)

BOWLS	30 MIN
MEDIUM	SERVES 4

Ingredients

4 slices nitrate-free bacon

1 medium sweet onion, diced

2 cloves garlic, minced

1 teaspoon salt

½ teaspoon ground black pepper

½ teaspoon paprika

1 ½ pounds grass-fed ground beef or 4 cups cooked black beans (see Big Batch Bean recipe, page 48)

1 medium tomato

¼ head romaine lettuce

Pickled jalapeños

Diced avocado

Kosher dill pickles

Special sauce

½ cup veganaise

2 tablespoons ketchup

1 tablespoon yellow mustard

1 tablespoon kosher dill pickle juice

Pinch of cayenne

Pepper

*Vegan option: use black beans

*Paleo option: use beef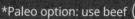

Directions:

Prep the bacon:

Cut the bacon into bite-sized pieces. Place in a large skillet over medium-high heat, and fry until crisp (about 3-4 minutes). In the meantime, combine the garlic, salt, pepper, and paprika in a small bowl.

Cook the beef:

Remove the bacon from the skillet and transfer it to a paper towel-lined plate. Reserve 1 tablespoon of the bacon fat in the skillet, and reheat over medium heat. Add the onion and cook until translucent, about 7 minutes. Add garlic and spice mix, and cook until fragrant, about 30 seconds. Add beef and cook until browned, stirring occasionally.

For black bean version:

Omit the bacon. Place 4 cups black beans on a parchment-lined baking sheet. Add spices and stir. Spread out on the baking sheet and mash with a potato masher or fork until roughly mashed. Drizzle with a little olive oil. Bake in a 400 degree oven for 20 minutes.

Prep the veggies & Special Sauce:

While the beef is simmering (or the beans are baking), dice the tomato, shred the lettuce, and prep the mayo. Place the Special Sauce ingredients in a small bowl and whisk to blend. The Special Sauce will keep in the fridge for up to two weeks in a covered container.

To serve:

Layer potatoes, then beef or beans, and top with bacon (if using), and a dollop of Special Sauce. Top with lettuce, tomato, avocado, pickles or pickled jalapeños, and other condiments of your choice.

Desserts

Macadamia Chocolate Chip Cookies

DESSERT

 35 MIN

EASY

YIELDS 20

Ingredients

1 cup Macadamia Nut Butter (page 41)

⅛ cup honey

¼ cup coconut oil

1 teaspoon vanilla extract

1 large egg, whisked

2 tablespoons coconut flour

Pinch of fine-grain sea salt

½ cup Enjoy Life® Mini Chocolate Chips

Directions:

Preheat the oven to 350 degrees.

Line 2 baking sheets with parchment paper.

In a large bowl, combine the macadamia nut butter, honey, coconut oil, vanilla, and egg. Mix by hand with a wooden spoon or spatula. Add the coconut flour and salt, and mix until incorporated, then fold in the chocolate chips. Refrigerate the batter until firm, about 10 to 12 minutes.

Drop balls of cookie dough onto the prepared baking sheets, using a medium-sized cookie scoop. Bake for 13-15 minutes, or until the cookies are golden. Remove from the oven and place on a rack to cool.

Honey Pistachio Ice Cream

DESSERT | **2.5 HRS**
largely unattended

EASY | YIELDS 1 PINT

Ingredients

1 cup raw, shelled pistachios, plus 1/3 cup roughly chopped, raw pistachios

1 (14-ounce) can full fat coconut milk

⅓ cup raw honey

1 teaspoon vanilla extract

Pinch of coarse sea salt

Directions:

Place the whole pistachios in a food processor, and pulse until they resemble a fine, flour-like consistency. (Don't over-process, or pistachios will turn into a paste.)

In a medium saucepan over medium heat, combine coconut milk, honey, vanilla, and salt. Slowly whisk in the pistachio flour. When well mixed, remove from the heat and cool. Place the mixture in a mixing bowl and cover. Refrigerate for at least 2 hours.

Place the mixture in an ice cream maker. Churn, following the manufacturer's instructions, to desired consistency. When there are about 2 minutes remaining, add the chopped pistachios and continue churning until the pistachios are mixed into the ice cream. Scoop out immediately so the ice cream doesn't freeze to the sides of the ice cream maker. This can be stored in the freezer for up to 3 weeks.

Macadamia Cookie Ice Cream

DESSERT

 2.5 HRS
largely unattended

EASY

YIELDS 1 PINT

Ingredients

14 ounce can full-fat coconut milk

⅓ cup organic honey

1 teaspoon vanilla extract

⅛ teaspoon ground cinnamon

Pinch of coarse sea salt

¼ cup unsweetened cocoa powder

3 Macadamia Chocolate Chip Cookies (page 123), frozen, then roughly chopped

Directions:

Warm the coconut milk, honey, vanilla, cinnamon, and salt over medium heat in a saucepan. Whisk until everything is well incorporated, then add cocoa powder and whisk again. Remove from heat and let cool. Place in a mixing bowl and cover with plastic wrap. Refrigerate for at least 2 hours or overnight.

Pour mixture into an ice cream maker. Churn, following the manufacturer's instructions, to desired consistency. Add the chopped cookies, and continue churning until the cookies are mixed throughout the ice cream. Scoop out immediately so the ice cream doesn't stick to the sides of the ice cream maker. Serve immediately. This can be stored in the freezer for up to 3 weeks.

  *Vegan option: use Agave nectar in place of honey

Chocolate Nut Butter Cups

DESSERT | **40 MIN** largely unattended

EASY | YIELDS 1 PINT

Ingredients

½ cup coconut oil, melted

½ cup raw cacao powder

2 tablespoons monkfruit sweetner

2 tablespoons coconut cream

¼ cup peanut, macadamia (page 41), cashew, or almond butter

Large pinch sea salt

Directions:

Place small parchment candy cups on a baking pan. In a small mixing bowl, combine coconut oil and cacao powder, and whisk until smooth. Stir in the monk fruit sweetner and coconut cream. Line the bottom of each cup with a thin layer of the mixture. Place in freezer for 5 minutes. Remove and spoon 1/3 teaspoon teaspoon nut butter into each cup. Top with remaining cacao mixture, and sprinkle with sea salt. Allow to harden in the fridge for 30 minutes before eating. Store in fridge to keep from melting.

Easy Cacao Pudding

DESSERT	**6 HRS** largely unattended
⚬ EASY	SERVES 4-6

Ingredients

1 (13 ounce) can full-fat coconut milk

½ cup hot water

4 ½ ounces pitted dates

½ cup raw cacao powder

¼ cup chia seeds

1 tablespoon melted coconut oil

2 teaspoons vanilla extract

¼ teaspoon sea salt

Dark chocolate shavings, unsweetened

Coconut flakes, or fresh berries for garnish

Directions:

Blend all ingredients (except the toppings) in a high-speed blender until smooth (about 45 seconds). Pour the pudding into serving bowls. Refrigerate for at least 6 hours before eating. Garnish with dark chocolate shavings, coconut flakes, or fresh berries. Top with coconut whipped milk frosting page 135, if you have some handy, and enjoy!

Chia Cashew Pudding

This recipe is inspired by my daughter Abigail, who is constantly experimenting with new recipes in the kitchen.

DESSERT | **30 MIN**

EASY | SERVES 4-6

Ingredients

1 ½ cups water

¼ cup chia seeds

6 large pitted dates, soaked in a bowl of hot water for 20 minutes, then drained

⅔ cup raw cashews, soaked in water for 4 hours, then drained

½ teaspoon ground cinnamon

½ teaspoon vanilla powder

Pinch of sea salt

Directions:

In a liquid measuring cup, combine the water and chia seeds. Set aside until mixture forms a gel, about 20 minutes.

In a blender, combine the dates with the cashews, cinnamon, vanilla powder, and salt. Pour in half of the chia gel. Puree until smooth. Mix in the remaining chia gel, and chill in the refrigerator before serving.

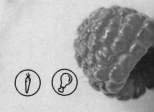

Coconut Cake

Pictured on page 120*

My sister Christine adapted this cake to be gluten free. It is delicious!

DESSERT	⏱ 1 HR
🍴 MEDIUM	SERVES 12

Ingredients

1 cup grass-fed butter

½ cup coconut oil, plus more for pans

1 ¼ cup almond flour

1 cup coconut flour

1 ¼ cup gluten-free all purpose flour

1 tablespoon plus 1 teaspoon baking powder

1 teaspoon salt

1 cup packed, unsweetened shredded coconut

1 ½ cups monk fruit sweetener

4 large whole eggs, plus 4 large egg whites

1 tablespoon pure vanilla extract

1 teaspoon almond extract

1 ½ cups unsweetened coconut milk

Coconut Milk Whipped Frosting (page135)

1 cup unsweetened coconut flakes, toasted, for garnish

1 cup chopped pecans, toasted, for garnish

½ cup almond paste (page ~~4~~) 41

Directions:

Preheat oven to 350 degrees. Grease two 9-inch round cake pans with coconut oil. Line the bottom of the pans with parchment paper and dust with flour. Tap out excess flour and set aside.

Sift flours into a medium bowl; whisk in baking powder and salt. Process shredded coconut in a food processor until finely chopped. Stir into flour mixture until incorporated and set aside.

Place butter, coconut oil, and monk fruit sweetener in the bowl of a stand-up mixer. Using the paddle attachment, beat until fluffy, about 4 minutes. Scrape down sides of bowl as needed. Add whole eggs, egg whites, vanilla and almond extracts. Beat until fluffy. With mixer on low speed, alternate adding flour mixture and coconut milk, beginning and ending with flour mixture. Mix well after each addition.

Divide batter equally between prepared pans. Use a spatula to smooth batter. Bake for about 35 minutes, until golden and a toothpick inserted into the center comes out clean. Rotate pans halfway through baking.

Cool pans on wire racks for 30 minutes, then invert the cakes onto the racks. Peel parchment off the cakes, and then re-invert the cakes to cool, top sides up.

Place one cake layer on a plate. Spread 1/2 cups Almond Paste (page 41) on the first layer.. Top with the second cake layer. Spread remaining frosting over the entire cake, using a spatula. Swirl to create a decorative look. Sprinkle entire cake with toasted coconut flakes and pecan pieces.

Coconut Milk Whipped Frosting

♀ EASY	YIELDS 2 CUPS

Ingredients

2 cans (13.5 ounces each) coconut cream, refrigerated for 24 hours

2 tablespoons honey

1 teaspoon vanilla extract

1 teaspoon almond extract

Directions:

Place bowl and beaters of stand-up mixer in the freezer to chill for 30 minutes or more. Remove the coconut milk from the fridge, without shaking. Scoop off the cream that has separated to the top, and place it in the chilled mixing bowl. The thinner liquid can be saved and used in smoothies. Beat the cream, honey, vanilla, and almond extracts on high until peaks form.

Snacks

Lemon-Poppyseed Collagen Bites

SNACKS

 2 HRS
largely unattended

EASY

YIELDS 20

Ingredients

1 tablespoon lemon zest

2 ¾ cups raw cashews

¼ cup monk fruit sweetener

Pinch of sea salt

1 teaspoon vanilla powder

2 tablespoons MCT oil powder

¼ cup coconut oil, melted

1 cup grass-fed beef collagen powder

2 tablespoons poppyseeds

Directions:

Line a baking sheet with parchment paper and set aside.

Place lemon zest, cashews, monk fruit sweetener, salt, vanilla powder, MCT powder, and coconut oil in food processor. Process until completely smooth. It may clump at first, but it will smooth out. When smooth, add the collagen powder, poppyseeds, and and remaining cashews, and process briefly to incorporate.

Roll into 2 tablespoon balls and place on the parchment paper-lined baking sheet. Freeze for 2 hours before serving. Store in an airtight container in the freezer and thaw at room temperature when ready to enjoy.

*Vegan option: use vegan collagen

Peanut Butter Energy Bites

These are reminiscent of my mom's famous "No Bake Cookies." My mom inspired me to be creative in the kitchen. There were constantly delicious smells coming from our kitchen!

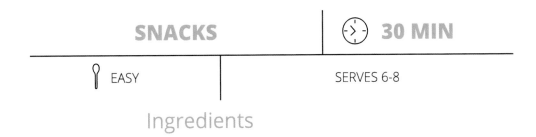

SNACKS	⏱ 30 MIN
🥄 EASY	SERVES 6-8

Ingredients

2 cups gluten-free rolled oats

2 cups unsweetened coconut flakes

1 cup hemp seeds

½ teaspoon sea salt

1 ¼ cups natural peanut butter

¼ cup raw honey

1 teaspoon vanilla extract

4 ounces Enjoy Life® mini chocolate chips

Directions:

Preheat oven to 300 degrees.

Line a large baking sheet with parchment paper, and place the oats, coconut flakes, hemp seeds, and salt in the center. Stir to combine, and flatten evenly over the surface. Bake for about 15 minutes, or until lightly toasted, stirring once.

Place the peanut butter, honey, and vanilla in the top of a double boiler or in a saucepan over another saucepan that has about 2 inches of water in it. Bring to a boil, and allow the peanut butter mixture to melt until smooth. Stir to combine.

Mix the dry ingredients and the peanut butter mixture together in a large mixing bowl. Cool for about 10 minutes before stirring in the chocolate chips. Roll into balls (about 1 heaping tablespoon per ball). Place onto parchment-lined baking sheets. Put the baking sheets in the refrigerator and chill until firm. Store in the refrigerator or freezer.

 *Vegan option: use coconut nectar, or brown rice syrup instead of honey

Almond Butter Granola Bars

SNACKS	⊙ **2 HRS** largely unattended
𝖸 EASY	SERVES 6-8

Ingredients

¼ cup honey

½ cup almond butter

2 tablespoons coconut oil

1 teaspoon pure vanilla extract

¼ cup raw pecans

¾ cup raw cashews

½ cup raw almonds

5 large pitted dates, soaked in warm water for 15 minutes

¼ cup shredded, unsweetened coconut flakes

½ cup dark chocolate pieces

OTHER NUTS OR SEEDS THAT CAN BE SUBSTITUTED:

Hazelnuts

Walnuts

Macadamia nuts

Brazil nuts

Pumpkin seeds

Sunflower seeds

Poppy seeds

Sesame seeds

*Vegan option: use coconut nectar, or brown rice syrup instead of honey

Directions:

Prepare a 9 x 13 inch baking dish by lining it with parchment paper.

In a small saucepan over medium heat, combine the honey, almond butter, coconut oil, and vanilla. Bring the mixture to a boil, then reduce the heat to low and continue simmering for 10 minutes.

In the meantime, pulse pecans, cashews, almonds, and dates in a food processor until nuts are coarsely chopped. Add the nuts into the honey mixture, and stir to blend. Cool for 5 minutes then add coconut flakes and chocolate chips in thoroughly. Spread mixture evenly in the prepared baking dish, pressing down with the back of a spoon. Pack down as tightly as possible so it holds together. Place in the freezer and allow to harden for 2 hours. Remove from the freezer and lift out of the pan, holding the edges of the parchment to lift. Cut into 12 rectangular bars with a

Apples & Nut Butter

My go-to snack when I'm on the road during my lunch time, or at the end of a work day before I make dinner, is apple slices and almond butter, cashew butter, or sunflower seed butter. This prevents a blood sugar crash and binge eating something that I will regret later!

SNACKS	⏱ 5 MIN
🥄 EASY	SERVES 1

Ingredients

Directions:

Dip and enjoy!

1 apple, sliced

4 tablespoons almond butter

Easy Hummus

My Uncle Murro taught me to use Navy Beans instead of garbanzo beans for a smooth hummus.

SNACKS	15 MIN
EASY	SERVES 2

Ingredients

2 cups Big Batch Beans (page 48) or canned navy beans or chickpeas

⅓ cup tahini

Juice of one lime

1 jalapeño pepper (optional)

2 medium cloves garlic

½ teaspoon cumin powder

¼ teaspoon sea salt

¼ cup olive oil

Directions:

Add the tahini, lime juice, jalapeno, and garlic to a food processor. Blend for about 1 minute, then add half of the beans, the cumin, and the sea salt. Blend again for another minute, then add the other half the beans. Puree, slowly adding 1/4 cup of olive oil into the food processor.

Drizzle with a little more olive oil and sprinkle with cayenne pepper. Serve with cut up veggies, chips, or crackers.

Spinach & Artichoke Dip

SNACKS

 30 MIN

EASY

YIELDS 2 CUPS

Ingredients

1 (16 ounce) package frozen spinach, thawed and drained

2 (14 ounce) cans quartered artichoke hearts, roughly chopped

Coarse sea salt and freshly ground pepper, to taste

1 cup raw roasted cashews

3 tablespoons extra virgin olive oil

1 teaspoon garlic powder

1 teaspoon onion powder

3 tablespoons nutritional yeast

½ teaspoon dried basil

¼ teaspoon cayenne pepper

Directions:

Preheat the oven to 350 degrees.

Combine the spinach, artichokes, and a pinch of salt in a large saucepan, then set over medium heat and heat through.

Place the cashews in a food processor and pulse until they are roughly chopped. Add the olive oil, garlic and onion powders, nutritional yeast, basil, cayenne pepper, salt, and pepper. Puree until smooth.

Combine the cashew mixture with the spinach mixture in the saucepan, and mix well. Simmer on low heat briefly to warm through. Place mixture in baking dish and bake for 15 minutes.

Serve with crackers, chips, or in a veggie wrap with other toppings for lunch. (Paleo "Tortilla" Wraps on page 35).

Spicy Guacamole

SNACKS

 10 MIN

EASY

YIELDS 1.5 CUPS

Ingredients

3 medium garlic cloves

1 jalapeño pepper, cored, seeded

3 ripe avocados, peeled, halved, and pitted

3 tablespoons fresh lemon juice

2 scallions (green onions), white bulb and 3 inches green, diced

1 teaspoon Tabasco® sauce

½ teaspoon sea salt

1 teaspoon ground black pepper

2 tablespoons chopped cilantro

Directions:

Drop the garlic and jalapeño pepper down the feed tube of a food processor while the motor is running. Process until finely chopped. Add 1 1/2 avocados and lemon juice; process until smooth. Scrape the mixture into a bowl, then add the remaining avocados and mash with a fork. Add the remaining ingredients. Mix thoroughly with a fork. Serve at room temperature within an hour or two.

JOURNAL EXERCISE | SELF-REFLECTION

Once you have gotten into a bit of a routine with this new way of meal planning and prep, cooking, and eating, take a moment to reflect on how you feel. Has anything changed for you when you think about how you feel now compared to when you got started eating like this?

JOURNAL EXERCISE | CELEBRATING

Take note of any differences you are aware of, and take a moment to journal about them. Celebrate the small victories; you might be cooking one day a week more than you used to, you might be planning meals instead of winging it, or you might be eating breakfast instead of running out the door. Even if you're only doing one thing different than before, that's huge! Often it's baby steps that will get you to where you want to be, so take time to celebrate your accomplishments, no matter how big or small they seem to you. Think about whether now is the time to incorporate something new into your routine. Making healthy lifestyle changes is a journey and takes time, so don't give up.

JOURNAL EXERCISE | GRATITUDE

Every morning when you wake up, try journaling 10 things for which you are grateful. They don't have to be major things. Sometimes I catch myself thinking of big things coming up in my life that make me feel "successful." These things should not be the focus here. When you take a few minutes to stop and pay attention, you begin to notice that it's the seemingly minor things for which to be grateful. Aspects such as our health and the fact that we breathe in and out without having to remind our bodies to do that are miracles in themselves.

The more you practice daily gratitude, the more joy you will find in your day-to-day life.

_____

_____

_____

_____

_____

_____

_____

_____

_____

_____

_____

_____

_____

_____

_____

_____

_____

_____

_____

_____

_____

JOURNAL EXERCISE | GOAL-SETTING

Take a moment to look at all of the areas of your life that are important to you. For example: spirituality, exercise, career, relationships, creativity, home environment, home cooking.

Now, rate your level of satisfaction with each area on a scale of 1-10, with 10 being excellent. Choose one area where you would like to find more satisfaction, and set a goal for this week to make one small step to improve that area of your life.

If, for example, it's your home environment, and you're tired of clutter, maybe you need to declutter for 10 minutes a day this week, choosing 1 thing to focus on in that 10 minutes. Set a timer, and stick to that task for the full 10 minutes. See how it feels.

If it's relationships, make a point to spend time with someone you enjoy being with this week.

You get the point... have fun creating more balance in your life and eating like this!

RESOURCES

Cookbooks that have inspired me over the years in developing the Eat Like This Diet:

VB 6, by Mark Bittman

Well Fed, by Melissa Joulwan

Against All Grains, by Danielle Walker

I Quit Sugar, by Sarah Wilson

The Paleo Kitchen, by Juli Bauer & George Bryant

If you enjoyed this cookbook and want to know more about 1:1 or group coaching:

- Visit my website: rgec.life
- Follow my Instagram: @rebekah_empower
- Find me on Facebook: Rebekah Eisner
- Follow me on Tik Tok: @rebekah_empower
- Follow me on You Tube: Rebekah Eisner